Down in the Jungle

Vivian French

Illustrated by
Selina Young

Orion
Children's Books

For Willow
with love

The stories from *Down in the Jungle*
originally appeared in *The Story House*
first published in Great Britain in 2004
by Orion Children's Books
This edition first published in 2012
by Orion Children's Books
a division of the Orion Publishing Group Ltd
Orion House
5 Upper St Martin's Lane
London WC2H 9EA
An Hachette UK Company

1 3 5 7 9 10 8 6 4 2

Text copyright © Vivian French 2004 and 2012
Illustrations copyright © Selina Young 2004
Designed by Louise Millar

A catalogue record for this book is available from the British Library

Printed and bound in China

The Orion Publishing Group's policy is to use papers that
are natural, renewable and recyclable products and made
from wood grown in sustainable forests. The logging and manu
facturing processes are expected to conform to the environmental
regulations of the country of origin.

www.orionbooks.co.uk

Contents

Down in the Jungle

It was a warm summer's evening. Down in the jungle the animals were gathered round the edge of the cool blue lake. The older animals were trying to doze, but the younger ones were hot and bothered and cross.

"I'm bored," said Monkey. He swung himself onto the lowest branch of a shady tree. "It's much too hot to sleep."

"Why don't I tell you your bedtime story now?" said his mother. "And you can go to bed when it's cooler."

Monkey nodded. "All right. But I want a LONG story!"

Mrs Monkey laughed. "I think you'll like this one. It's about a clever little monkey, just like you!"

"OK." Monkey folded his arms. "I'm ready!"

Snap!

It was early in the morning, but Monkey was awake and swinging through the trees.

"I'm going fishing today!" he sang. "I'm going fishing today!"

Bear Cub was waiting for
Monkey on the river bank.
He had two fishing rods and
a bucket of worms.

"Are you ready, Monkey?"
he asked.

"Yes!" said Monkey.

They fished for five
minutes …

and they caught
nothing at all.

They fished for ten
minutes …

and they caught
nothing at all.

They fished for fifteen
minutes …

and they caught
nothing at all.

"Where have the fish gone?"
asked Monkey.

"I don't know," said Bear Cub.
"I'll jump in the river and look."
He jumped into the water.

"Ooof!" he said. "It's very cold."

"Any fish?" asked Monkey.

"No," said Bear Cub. "Only green
weed and a long brown log."

"Maybe," said Monkey, "we'd catch more fish if we stood on the log?"

"Good idea," said Bear Cub. He swam towards the long brown log.

The long brown log opened a huge toothy mouth ...

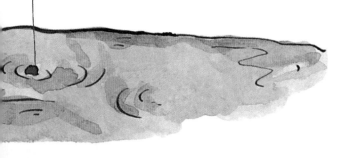

Snap!

Bear Cub was caught by his tail. "Help!" he shouted. "Help!"

"Be quiet," said the crocodile, and he kept his teeth shut tight. "I'm going to cook you and eat you for my tea."

Monkey was watching, and he shook his head.

"Hey! Crocodile!" Monkey called.

"What do you want?" Crocodile asked, and he kept his teeth shut tight on Bear Cub's tail.

"I just wondered if you knew how to make my granny's bear cub stew," said Monkey.

"What sort of stew is that?"
asked Crocodile, and he kept his
teeth shut tight on Bear Cub's tail.

"It's the most delicious stew
ever," said Monkey. "But you have
to have a pineapple."

"A pineapple?" said Crocodile.
"Where would I get a pineapple?"

Monkey swung away into the
jungle. Soon he was back with
a big yellow pineapple, and he
put it down on the river bank.

Crocodile's eyes lit up.
"Give it to me," he said, and
he still kept his teeth shut tight
on Bear Cub's tail.

"Oh no," said Monkey. "For bear
cub stew you need mangoes too."

"Mangoes?" said Crocodile.
"Where would I get mangoes?"

Monkey swung away into the
jungle.

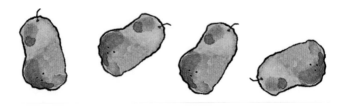

Soon he was back with four soft sweet mangoes, and he put them down on the river bank.

Crocodile's eyes shone. "Give them to me," he said, and he kept his teeth shut tight as tight on Bear Cub's tail.

"Oh no," said Monkey. "For bear cub stew you need coconuts too."

"Coconuts?" said Crocodile. "Where would I get coconuts?"

Monkey swung away into the jungle.

Soon he was back with six hard hairy coconuts.

Crocodile's eyes sparkled. "Give them to me," he said, and he kept a tight hold of Bear Cub's tail.

"No," said Monkey. "You haven't once said please. I'm going to eat them myself."

"Please!"

roared the crocodile and
his mouth opened wide.

"Please!"

"Here you are, then," said
Monkey. He threw a coconut
as hard as he could right into
Crocodile's wide open mouth.

"Hup! Hup! Hup!"
hiccupped Crocodile.

"Ho ho ho!"
laughed Monkey.

"Thank you, Monkey," said Bear Cub, as he pulled himself out of the river.

Monkey and Bear Cub took the pineapple and the mangoes and went to have a picnic.

They left the rest of the coconuts for Crocodile, just in case he ever wanted to make Monkey's granny's coconut crumble.

As Mrs Monkey finished her story, Monkey jumped up. "Hoo hoo!" he shouted. "Monkeys are the best."

"No they're not," said a voice from below. "In my dad's story the monkey isn't clever at all!"

Monkey saw a little elephant looking up at him.
"Hello," he said. "Do you think your dad would tell me his story?"

The little elephant nodded. "Come with me!"

Before his mother could say a word Monkey was running ahead of the little elephant to where her father was cooling his toes at the edge of the lake.

"Dad!" called the little elephant. Tell us about the elephant who didn't have any friends!"

"Harrumph," said Mr Elephant. "Very well. But then you must go to sleep, my dear." He looked at the monkey. "And you'd better sit on my head. Lakes can be dangerous for a little monkey."

The Elephant Who Had No Friends

The lion and the cheetah and the monkey and the elephant were friends. They played together, and they had swimming parties in the great blue lake.

But one day they had an argument.

"I'm the best in all the jungle!" said the lion. "I've got the biggest roar!

Roaaaar!"

"Huh," said the cheetah. "I can run faster than any of you." He ran round the great blue lake and back in no time at all. "See?" he said.

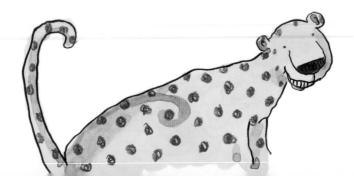

"But you can't climb trees, can you?" said the monkey.

He swung himself into a banana tree and climbed to the top. "See?" he said.

"Rubbish!" said the elephant. "I'm the best because I'm the strongest!"

He picked up the lion and threw him into the great blue lake.

Splash!!!!

Then he threw the cheetah.

Splash!!!!

Then he threw the monkey.

Splash!!!!

"See?" said the elephant.

The lion and the cheetah and the monkey dragged themselves out of the water.

"That was a horrible thing to do," said the lion.

"You're mean," said the cheetah.

"We don't want to be friends with you any more," said the monkey.

"Oh dear," said the elephant. "Maybe I shouldn't have done that. Never mind, we'll be friends again soon."

But he was **wrong.**

The lion and the cheetah and the monkey didn't want to be friends with a show-off elephant who threw them in the great blue lake.

The elephant was lonely. He walked sadly through the grass to the great blue lake. As the elephant came nearer he could hear the lion laughing. He peered through the trees.

"They don't miss me at all," he said, and a big tear trickled down his trunk.

He was just about to turn round when something caught his eye. It wasn't the lion diving from a rock, or the cheetah paddling, or the monkey splashing .

Something was creeping slowly, slowly … nearer and nearer to the monkey.

Something was slowly, slowly … opening its mouth full of long sharp teeth …

The elephant charged.
"Trumpetty Trumpetty Trumpetty!"

He scooped up the crocodile, and threw it into the middle of the great blue lake.

The lion and the cheetah and the monkey stared. Then they swam and splashed and paddled towards the elephant.

"Hurrah!" they shouted.
"You're the best friend ever!"

"Thank you," the elephant said.
He coughed a small cough.
"I'm very sorry I threw you
in the great blue lake. I promise I
won't do it again."

"And I won't boast about having the best roar ever," said the lion.

"And I won't show off my super speedy running," said the cheetah.

"Why don't I fetch us some bananas?" said the monkey. "Then we can have a party!"

"A best friends party?" said the elephant hopefully.

"Yes!" said the lion and the cheetah and the monkey.

And they did.

"That's a good story," the monkey said. "But I'd never get caught like that." He was about to swing down to the ground when he saw Mrs Tiger padding towards him with her two cubs.

He pulled at the elephant's enormous ear. "Mr Elephant, could you tell us another story? Just until Mrs Tiger has been to the lake and back?"

The tiger cubs heard him. "A story?" they squeaked. "Oh, we want to hear it!"

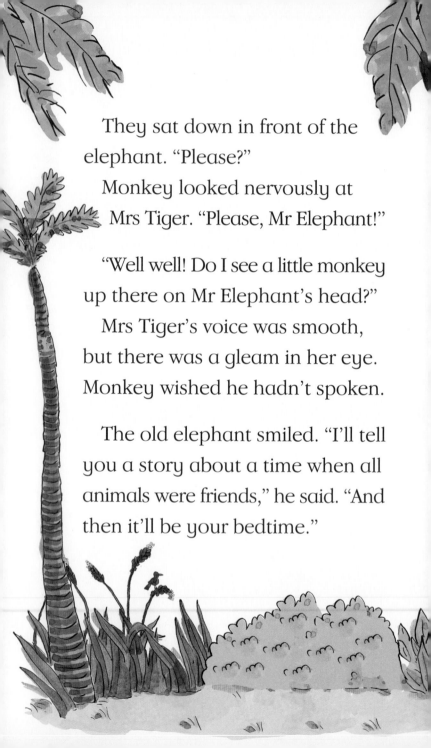

They sat down in front of the elephant. "Please?"

Monkey looked nervously at Mrs Tiger. "Please, Mr Elephant!"

"Well well! Do I see a little monkey up there on Mr Elephant's head?"

Mrs Tiger's voice was smooth, but there was a gleam in her eye. Monkey wished he hadn't spoken.

The old elephant smiled. "I'll tell you a story about a time when all animals were friends," he said. "And then it'll be your bedtime."

Why the Giraffe has a Long Neck

In the beginning of the beginning
all the animals looked the same.

The tigers didn't have stripes.

The elephants didn't have trunks.

The monkeys didn't climb trees.

Even the giraffes looked the
same as everyone else.
All the animals lived in the
big green forest, and all the
animals were friends.

The elephants and the monkeys played hide and seek. The tigers and the hippos went on picnics.

The lions and the crocodiles told each other stories.

The giraffes were too shy to play, but they enjoyed watching the other animals.

Every day was a holiday.

But then it rained.

It rained and it rained
and it rained.

The animals began to worry that
the forest would turn into a lake,
and they met to decide what to do.

"We're going to grow long noses so that we can breathe under water," said the elephants.

"We're going to learn how to climb trees so the water won't reach us," said the monkeys.

"We're going to grow golden fur and live in the sandy deserts," said the lions.

"We're going to grow stripes,"
said the tigers.

"We're going to learn to swim,"
said the hippos.

"We're going to learn to swim
too," said the crocodiles. "Then
we won't mind if the whole world
is a lake."

"What shall we do?" the giraffes asked each other.

Some thought they should grow long noses like the elephants.

Some thought they should climb trees like the monkeys. Some thought they should follow the lions into the deserts.

Some thought they should learn to swim. They couldn't make up their minds.

"Let's not decide just yet," said the oldest giraffe. "Let's wait and see."

So the giraffes waited. They peered over bushes, and stretched up and up to peep through the branches of the trees.

"Do we want long noses like the elephants ?" they asked.

"Looks funny to me," said the oldest giraffe.

"Ooooh!" said a little giraffe. "The hippos and the crocodiles are swimming!"

"Looks cold in that water," said the oldest giraffe.

"The lions are yellow! The tigers are stripy!" The monkeys can swing from tree to tree!"

"No, no, no," said the oldest giraffe. "I don't fancy swinging at all."

"Look!" shouted the little giraffe.

"What at?" asked the oldest giraffe. "Haven't we seen all the other animals and their funny ways?"

"Look at us!" said the little giraffe. "Our legs have stretched! And so have our necks!"

The little giraffe was right. All the giraffes had long legs and long necks.

"Hmm," the oldest giraffe said. "I'd say we look rather fine.

"And if there is a flood," said the little giraffe, "we'll be too tall to drown."

"Of course we will," said the oldest giraffe. "I was just about to say that."

So all the giraffes kept their long long necks … even though the forest never did turn into a huge lake.

"That's why I climb trees," Monkey said proudly.

"And that's why I've got a trunk," said the little elephant.

"And that's why we've got stripes," said the tiger cubs. "But what about roaring? Tigers roar **ever** so loudly."

Their mother frowned. "Hush, children. Don't you remember the story I told you?"

"A story about roaring?" the little elephant asked hopefully. "I bet it's wonderful!"

"Ma tells the best stories ever!" squeaked the cubs.

"You want me to tell your friends about the five little tigers?" Mrs Tiger purred.

Before the cubs could answer the little elephant said. "Oh yes, Mrs Tiger! And Monkey does too."

Monkey had been hoping Mrs Tiger would forget him, but he waved a paw. "Yes please," he said.

Mrs Tiger smiled a sharp toothed smile. "Very well."

The Tiger Who Couldn't Roar

There was once a tiger who couldn't roar. When it was time for lessons, Little Tiger One Stripe roared a great big roar.

"Grrrr!!!"

Little Tiger Two Stripes roared a bigger roar.

"Grrrr!!!"

Little Tiger Three Stripes roared a huge roar that made the parrots shake on top of the trees.

"Grrrr!!!"

Little Tiger Four Stripes roared such a big roar that the parrots flew away.

"Grrrrrr!"

But when Fiver tried to roar, all that came out was a squeak.

"Eeek."

Old Tiger looked cross. "Fiver," he said. "That is no noise for a tiger. Please roar properly."

But Fiver couldn't. **"Eeek,"** he said. **"Eeek. Arrrk. Eeek."**

His brothers began to laugh. "Silly Fiver," they said. Fiver's whiskers drooped.

When the lesson was over, four little tigers bounced away. Fiver trailed behind them.

"Let's play hide and seek!" said Little Tiger One Stripe.

"I'll roar when I find you," said Little Tiger Two Stripes.

"Us too!" said Little Tiger Three Stripes and Little Tiger Four Stripes.

"Can I play?" asked Fiver.

"No," said Little Tiger One Stripe. "You can't roar."

"Oh," said Fiver, and he went to sit behind a rock.

"I'm no good at being a tiger,"
he thought. "I'll go into the jungle,
and I won't ever come back."

He hadn't gone far when
he heard a noise.

"Eeek! Squeak! Help! Eeek!"

A mouse was running up
the path, and behind her was
a long spotty snake.

"*Sssss!*" hissed the snake.
"Come and be my breakfast,
little mou*sssse!*"

Fiver took a deep breath. "I'm a no-good tiger," he said to himself. "I don't mind if a snake eats me for his breakfast. I don't care!" He jumped at the snake.

"Eeek! Leave that mouse alone. **Eeeek!"**

The snake stopped, and stared and began to laugh. It laughed so much that it tied itself up in a knot.

"Tee hee hee! A tiger that *squeaksss* like a mou*ssse!* That's so funny I don't mind losing my breakfa*sssssst!*" It untied itself and slid away.

Fiver was glad the snake hadn't eaten him, but he didn't like being laughed at.

"Eeek!" It was the mouse. "Thank you!"

Fiver looked down. "It was nothing," he said.

The mouse came closer. "What's the matter?"

Fiver sighed. "I'm a no-good tiger. I can't roar. I can only squeak."

The mouse looked offended. "There's nothing wrong with squeaking."

"I didn't mean to be rude," said Fiver. "But mice squeak. Tigers roar."

"You did a very brave thing with only a squeak," said the mouse, and she ran away into the grass.

"Grrrrr! Grrrrr! Grrrrrr!"

There was a rustling and a crashing. Three of Fiver's little brothers came tumbling out of the bushes.

"Quick!" they said. "There's a long spotty snake and it's trying to catch Little Tiger Four Stripes!"

"Run! Run! Run!"

Fiver looked at them in surprise. "A long spotty snake?" he said.

"Yes!" said Little Tiger One Stripe. "It's hissing and opening its mouth wide wide wide!"
And all three rushed away.

Fiver stood still and listened. The jungle was quiet.

"Eeek!" squeaked Fiver. "Mouse – can you hear me?"

"Of course," said the mouse. "There's no need to shout."

Fiver saw her sitting near his paws.

"Do you know where my brother is?" he asked.

The mouse nodded. "He'll be a spotty snake's breakfast if you don't hurry," she said. "This way!"

In and out of the bushes they went, and there was a scared little tiger balancing in the branches of a tree.

The long spotty
snake was slithering
nearer …

and nearer …

when…

**"Eeek! Aark!
Eeek!"** squeaked
Fiver.

The snake looked down at him. *"Sssss!"* it hissed. "Squeaking won't work this time. Go away!"

Fiver's whiskers twitched.

Fiver began to feel angry.

Fiver began to feel very angry.

Fiver began to feel very angry indeed.

He opened his mouth…

And he roared!

He roared so loudly that
the leaves shivered, the tree
trembled – and the long spotty
snake slipped and fell to the
ground with a

Thump!

"Ouch!" it hissed crossly,
and slid away.

Little Tiger Four Stripes and
Fiver hurried back home.

"Fiver saved me!" shouted Little Tiger Four Stripes. "He roared so loudly that the long spotty snake fell out of the tree!"

"Well done, Fiver," said Old Tiger. "You're a brave little tiger. Show us how you roar!"

Fiver opened his mouth and roared.

"Eeek! Aark! Eeek!"

Everybody laughed as Mrs Tiger finished her story.

"A very fine story, Mrs Tiger," Mr Elephant said. "Now you'll be wanting to get your cubs to bed, so I'll say good night."

Mrs Tiger smoothed her whiskers. "Thank you," she said, "but there's no hurry." She stared up at Monkey, licking her lips. "Isn't it time you were going home?"

Monkey began to tremble.

"Harrumph!" Mr Elephant looked thoughtfully at Mrs Tiger. "I don't think Monkey needs to go home just yet. We might have just one more story."

Monkey sighed in relief.

"It's a story about sharing," said Mr Elephant. He waved his trunk at the lake. "All of us have to share the water, and it's better to share with friends."

"We know that, Dad," said the little elephant. "Tell us the story!"

The Grumpy Lion

Long ago there was a lion who was not a nice lion. He was grumpy, he was bossy, and he hated sharing. He lived alone in a beautiful cave, and he sat in the doorway and grumbled when any other animals went past.

"Look at that! The elephants are tramping through my grass! The giraffes are eating my leaves. The monkeys are swinging from my creepers!"

The lion was never pleased to see anyone, so when a small mouse wandered up to his cave he frowned a terrible frown.

"What do you want? Run away or I'll eat you for my dinner!"

The mouse sat up and smiled.

"I'm looking for somewhere to live," he said. "I heard you had a beautiful cave, and I thought you might like to share it. I don't take up much room, and I'm good at telling jokes."

The lion frowned even more fiercely.

"What?" he roared. "Share my beautiful cave with a mouse? Never! No!"

"Oh well," said the mouse,
"I'll be off then." And he went
away into the jungle.

The lion saw the elephants tramping through the grass, and he roared.

"Hey! Elephants! A horrible mouse wants to live with me in my beautiful cave! Isn't that so silly?"

"A mouse? Wanting to live with you?" the elephants said. "Bless our trunks and tails! We wouldn't want to live with you. You're much too grumpy."

The lion sat down again. "What do they mean?" he said. "I'm not grumpy. I'm angry, and it's all because of that horrible mouse."

He grumbled and rumbled until he saw the giraffes eating the leaves, and he roared.

"Hey! Giraffes! A horrible mouse wants to live with me in my beautiful cave! Isn't that so silly?"

"A mouse? Wanting to live
with you?" the giraffes said. "Bless
our big brown spots! We wouldn't
want to live with you. You're
much too bossy."

The lion sat down again. "Whatever do they mean?" he said. "I'm not bossy. I'm angry, and it's all because of that horrible mouse."

He grumbled and he rumbled until he saw the monkeys swinging on the vines, and he roared, "Hey! Monkeys! A horrible mouse wants to live with me in my beautiful cave! Isn't that so silly?"

"A mouse? Wanting to live with you?" the monkeys said. "Bless our ears and noses! We wouldn't want to live with you. You hate sharing anything with anybody."

The lion sat down to think. "What do they mean?" he said. "The elephants said they wouldn't want to live with me. The giraffes didn't want to. And neither did the monkeys. Oh, my teeth and whiskers! Nobody likes me!"

The lion felt very sorry for himself. "Maybe I should have let that mouse share my beautiful cave," he said sadly. "Maybe his jokes would cheer me up. It's too late now. I expect he's gone to live with the elephants. Or the giraffes. Or the monkeys."

"No I haven't!" said a small squeaky voice. "Here I am!"

"Oh!" said the lion. "Hello, Mouse! Do please come in!"

What was the very first joke that the mouse told the lion? Why, that he had a hundred aunts and uncles and brothers and sisters, and that they were all coming to share the lion's beautiful cave.

And do you know what? The lion didn't mind one bit.

The little elephant yawned.
"I like them being friends. You're
my friend, aren't you, Monkey?'

Monkey was looking at the
trees where his mother was
waiting. They seemed a very long
way away. "Oh," he said.

Mrs Tiger stood up. "Maybe the
monkey would like to walk home
with us? It's not safe for little animals
to be out on their own so late."

"You're right, Mrs Tiger." The
elephant nodded, and Monkey held
on tightly. Was he going to have
to walk with the tigers?

"I'll take Monkey home."
Mr Elephant said.

Monkey let out a huge sigh of
relief. "Thank you," he said.
"Thank you."

Mrs Tiger sniffed. "Mr Elephant
is much too kind. Come along,
cubs. We'll go to the lake instead."

"Phew," Monkey whispered to
himself. "Phew!"

Mr Elephant walked slowly and
steadily towards the trees, his
daughter by his side.